Presented to

"Baby" Plato

On the occasion of

Angela Viser

From

5/20/02

Date

Celebration of Life

Tracie Peterson

Illustrated by Lisa Totman

PROMISE
PRESS

An Imprint of Barbour Publishing

ISBN 1-57748-577-7

Published by Barbour Publishing, Inc., P.O. Box 719, Uhrichsville, Ohio 44683
http://www.barbourbooks.com

 Member of the
Evangelical Christian
Publishers Association

Printed in China.

Celebration of Life

Dedicated with love to
Jennifer, Julie, and Erik—
my celebrations of life.
Mom

Baby's Name: _____

Born: _____ at _____:_____ A.M./P.M.

Weight: _____ lbs. _____ ozs.

Height: _____ inches

Color of Hair: _____

Color of Eyes: _____

Comments: _____

_____

_____

_____

A Celebration of Life

Gather 'round and celebrate the joy that has been given.
A gift of love—of flesh and blood. A tiny bit of heaven.

See the wonder of it all, and marvel at the sight,
Share the happiness we know, celebrate the life.

Make memories of the times to come, of hours and days and years.
Mark down each step, each task, each word—the laughter and the tears.

For a celebration of life is such, that one must never be
In too big a hurry to stop and smell. . .to feel. . .to touch. . .to see.

Yes, gather 'round and celebrate the life that has been given,
A gift of love—of hope eternal. Our tiny bit of heaven.

There is a wonder in the birth
of a baby that takes us beyond
the mundane and into the realm
of the divine.

> May your father and mother be glad; may she who gave you birth rejoice!
>
> Proverbs 23:25

The Rhythm of Life

The first time I ever saw my son was via the modern technology of sonograms. When I was only a few weeks pregnant, the technician applied the sonogram to learn the due date of my child. I lay there in anticipation of learning that date, but I assumed that it was too early to see anything of the baby I carried inside me. With a smile, the woman operating the machine said, "Well, there he is."

I glanced up to see a black smudge on the monitor screen. "Not much of a looker," I said, laughing.

"No, but he or she is clearly there with a strong, steady heartbeat."

I was dumbfounded. "How can you tell?"

She leaned closer to the screen and pointed. "See this tiny flashing light?" I nodded. "That, Mrs. Peterson, is your son or daughter's heart, and that flash you see is the heart beating."

I watched in wonder. A tiny light in darkness, pulsating and flashing with the rhythm of life. Even now, years later, I marvel at the wonder of that beating heart and rejoice in the awesome pleasure of motherhood.

WEE WILLIE WINKIE

An infant's wants should be attended to without waiting for him to cry. At first, a babe cries merely from a sensation of suffering—because food, warmth, or other comforts necessary to his young existence, are withheld; but when he finds crying is the only means of attracting attention, he soon gets in the habit of crying for everything. To avoid this, his wants should be attended to, whether he demand it or not.

Lydia Maria Child,
The Mother's Book

Little Lamb

Little Lamb, who made thee?
Dost thou know who made thee?
Gave thee life and bid thee feed
By the stream and o'er the mead;
Gave thee clothing of delight,
Softest clothing wooly bright;
Gave thee such a tender voice,
Making all the vales rejoice!
Little Lamb, who made thee?
Dost thou know who made thee?

Little Lamb, I'll tell thee,
Little Lamb, I'll tell thee!
He is calléd by thy name,
For he calls himself a Lamb;
He is meek and he is mild,
He became a little child;
I a child and thou a lamb,
We are calléd by his name.
Little Lamb, God bless thee.
Little Lamb, God bless thee.

William Blake

Ten Things Your New Baby Needs

1. Watch him sleep. Newborns need lots of rest. Take time to relax while he does.

2. Feed him. This isn't a chore—it's a very special time of nurturing and loving that will bond you together forever.

3. Change his diapers and clothes. See how intricate and tiny his little arms and legs are?

4. Bathe him. A warm bath in the protection of loving arms makes for a special time between baby and parents.

5. Play with him. Even newborns need stimulation. Gently bicycle the baby's legs in tiny peddling motions. Slowly and gently bring hands together as if clapping. Introduce rattles and other non-toxic, baby-safe toys.

6. Talk to your baby. Babies need to hear your voice. It reassures, calms, and translates love in a powerful way.

7. Cuddle and rock your baby, just for the pleasure of it. The troubles of the world seem very unimportant when you're rocking your baby.

8. Give him a place of quiet rest. Just as newborns need stimulation, they also need to be given times of non-stimulation.

9. Limit the number of new visitors in the life of your baby. Visitors can be overwhelming to infants, so don't just pass baby from person to person.

10. Love your baby and each other. Gently stroke baby's cheek, kiss him, and hold him close. Newborns need love and so do adults. Moms and dads gain as much from this as do the infants. Take time for each other, to encourage and help one another, so that you can truly celebrate the gift you've been given.

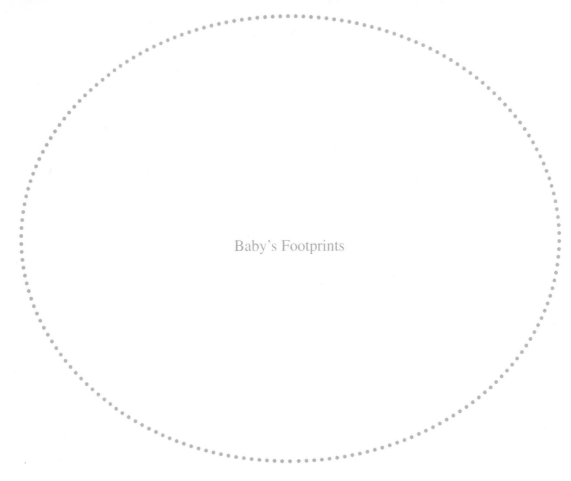

Baby's Footprints

Train a child in the way he should go,
and when he is old he will not turn from it.
Proverbs 22:6

Nighty Night

Sun goes down, moon comes up
Stars are in the sky.
Baby's going nighty night,
Nighty-night, beddie-bye.

Day is done, the time has come
To close your sleepy eyes.
Baby's going nighty night,
Nighty-night, beddie-bye.

Dream your dreams, while angels sing
and whisper peaceful sighs,
Baby's going nighty night,
Nighty-night, beddie-bye.

Sons are a heritage from the LORD,
children a reward from him.
Like arrows in the hands of a warrior
are sons born in one's youth.
Blessed is the man whose quiver is full of them.
Psalm 127:3-5

The First Week of a Baby's Life

· The first week of a baby's life will mostly be spent in sleep. Experts say that most babies will sleep between seventy-five and eighty-five percent of their day, in four to six naps. New mothers should seek rest as much as possible during these times.

· During the first week, baby may require from six to eight feedings, taking only a few ounces of a bottle at a time or nursing for only ten to fifteen minutes.

· Babies at this age are sensitive to sound, and sudden noises will cause them to jump. They will also be sensitive to touch and might be overstimulated by too many noises, strangers handling them, and other interruptions.

Thoughts on our baby's first week

_____

_____

_____

_____

_____

_____

_____

_____

_____

_____

_____

_____

_____

_____

Photograph

Precious Moments

A friend of mine once told me that feeding time was her favorite time to spend with her new baby. She made it a ritual. She would put on soothing music and find a quiet place to sit. She would make sure the baby's diaper was changed and that Baby was warm enough, and then they would share the quiet moment together. She said, "In those short moments of our lives, I could daydream and wonder about the things my child would do with her life. I could pray and ask God's blessings. But most of all, I shared a connection with my child that nothing else came close to."

Take advantage of the little things in the life of your baby. Allow yourself time to enjoy feeding, bathing, or cuddling your baby. Don't hurry through bedtime in order to get your kitchen clean or do another load of laundry. Your work will still be there in years to come—but your baby will be grown. Take time now to celebrate.

Perfect Proof

Baby hands and baby toes,
Baby eyes and baby nose,
Tiny lips so soft and sweet
Knit together so complete.
What a wonder from above
Perfect proof that God is love.

Photograph

A Soothing Technique

Swaddling" is spoken of in the Bible. This is the process of wrapping a baby securely in a blanket or other soft cloth. This wrapping gives the baby a sense of security. Oftentimes crying infants, who appear to have no other needs, are comforted by being swaddled. Native Americans often carried their babies in a cradleboard on their backs and even when not carrying them, they would have the baby secured in this type of swaddling. Hospital nurseries practice swaddling, as you may have seen, wrapping the babies quite snugly in receiving sized blankets and leaving them as little bundled forms with nothing more than their faces showing. So the next time your baby appears to be crying for no reason, you might try this method of comforting.

Children are the anchors that hold a mother to life.

Sophocles

Father, may we always see
Our children from Your view,
And set the example of trusting You
In all we say and do.

So that when our lives are finished
And our final breath is drawn,
Your loving word and mercy
In our children will live on.

I Samuel 1:27-28

I prayed for this child, and the LORD has granted me what I asked of him. So now I give him to the LORD.

God's Vision

When I was four and a half months pregnant, I got the bad news that something was wrong with the child I carried. Blood tests proved the possibility that my child would be deformed, retarded, and probably die very young. My husband and I were devastated, and as the doctor pressed for more testing, the only words I had from the medical community were, "Consider abortion. You're young. You can have other children. Why burden the world with another handicapped child?"

I've never been more devastated, nor more dependent upon God. This child for whom I had longed, loved while even yet unborn, was already given a death sentence by the very people who should have fought to save his life. Through much prayer we faced the birth of this child with anxious anticipation. And always God seemed only to say, "Trust Me. All is well."

When Erik was born, Mother's Day 1989, he cried out with a mighty voice as if to say, "I am here. You were wrong. I will live." There was absolutely nothing wrong with my baby. He had no monstrous deformities. No retardation. No terminal condition. He was alive and well and everything that we had ever dreamed a child could be. Proof in a six-pound, twelve-ounce bundle, that God sees more than humans do.

For you created
my inmost being; you knit me
together in my mother's womb.
I praise you because I am
fearfully and
wonderfully made; your works are
wonderful, I know that full well.

Psalm
139:13-14

Babies at One Month

· Babies at one month of age are rapidly becoming more complex.

· They can often roll from side to side and partway onto their backs at this age.

· Babies at this age are awake more.

· Most babies at this age will recognize the voices of their parents or primary caretaker.

· The one-month-old baby will start to expect feedings at regular intervals.

· Crying deliberately for attention becomes more apparent.

· One-month-old babies smile at voices or other stimuli.

*Thoughts on
our baby at
one month*

Photograph

Reflections of a Mother's Heart

Date: _____

Things I want you to know about me:

_____
_____
_____

Things I want to say about you:

_____
_____
_____

Things I hope for your future:

_____
_____
_____

My prayer for you:

_____
_____
_____

Children are the hands by which we take hold of heaven.

Henry Ward Beecher

My little one,
my little one,
A treasure from above
A heritage—a legacy
A gift of God's
own love.

Mother's Love

In a mother's heart there grows a seed
Of love that never dies.
And through that love she gives her children
Wings on which to rise.

Wings that take them high and far
And bring them back to find
That the garden of a mother's love
Is indeed a love that binds.

A woman giving birth to a child has pain
because her time has come; but when her baby is born
she forgets the anguish because of her joy
that a child is born into the world.

John 16:21

The Joy Lives On

I remember very little about the actual pain of laboring to deliver three children. I remember certain events surrounding the pregnancy, images that come to mind to remind me of the momentous occasion of their birth, but the intensity of delivery pain has faded from my mind. As soon as I saw the face of each of my children, the pain seemed insignificant and unimportant. The waiting was over, and now in my arms I held that precious new life that had grown so steadily within me for nine long months.

I still remember the pain existed. And I know that more pain will come in the years to come. But I believe in the long run, the pain will be worth it. The outcome will outweigh the suffering.

In many ways, we will give birth to those babies over and over again. Their first step. . .their first injury. . .their first heartache. . .their first solo decision. Each time we feel the pain of delivery—but in the long run we rejoice with them as they enter a new phase of life. The pain is soon forgotten, but the joy lives on.

Celebrate the new things
that God brings to your life
and to your child's!

29

Babies have a way of making us take a reality check.
The reality is:

· They are needy
· They are helpless
· They are dependent upon us for everything—including
acceptance and love.

To be blessed with a newborn life is to know great happiness. The English essayist Joseph Addison once said, "The grand essentials to happiness in this life are something to do, something to love, and something to hope for." A newborn baby is the epitome of all three. There is always something to do with a newborn. They are very easy to love and very in need of love. And in them is the hope of all our tomorrows.

Family Photograph

Here am I,
and the children the
LORD has given me.

Isaiah 8:18

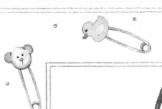

Babies at Two Months

· By two months, most babies are getting into a regular routine
and often setting the tempo for the entire family.

· Babies drink as much as thirty-six ounces of milk a day by this point
and usually set themselves in a cycle of demanding food
every four hours during the daytime.

· Most babies at this point will weigh at least eleven pounds and will sleep
as much as six to nine hours through the night, skipping night feedings.

· Babies will be awake as much as ten to twelve hours during the day,
usually taking several short naps.

Give a little love to a child,
and you get a great deal back.
John Ruskin

Thoughts on our baby at two months

_____

_____

_____

_____

_____

_____

_____

_____

_____

_____

_____

_____

_____

Photograph

Mommy's Baby

Mommy's baby becomes her child
While Mommy washes and cleans the tile.
But I don't want to miss a second of your growing,
While scurrying, hurrying, always on the run.
So baby child come, here's a kiss and a hug.
Let's take time to play. . .*before* the dishes are done.

Carolyn R. Scheidies (© 1999)

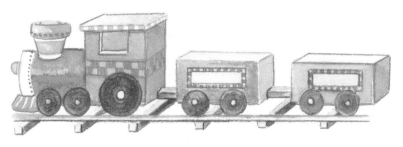

Gentleness is a sort of mild atmosphere;
and it enters into a child's soul,
like the sunshine into the rosebud, slowly
but surely expanding it into beauty and vigor.

Lydia Maria Child,
The Mother's Book

A Lighthouse for My Children

Deuteronomy 6:5-7

If I could describe myself as some symbolic object for the benefit of my children, it would have to be a lighthouse. Lighthouses are firmly fixed, stationary guards. They are sometimes poetically beautiful, sometimes scarred by the elements, but always steadfast in their duties. They are to warn, to caution, to protect. They stand with warning light offering a call: "Heed me! Watch out! Be warned!"

But lighthouses send their light from the inside out. If there is no light in my heart, I can't be a beacon to my children. If I fail to maintain my spiritual growth and care, I cannot reflect the truth that might one day steer them through trouble.

Then, too, I can only display light for them to see. I can't make them heed the warning or see the truth. And like the lighthouse that must stand fast, I will often see them make their own choices, refuse the warning, and crash on the rocks below.

A lighthouse is a symbol of guardianship, a protector that is consistent and unmoved. I would like to be that for my children.

Love the LORD your God with all your heart, and with all your soul, and with all your strength. These commandments that I give you today are to be upon your hearts. Impress them on your children.

Babies at Three Months

· Babies at this age often start cooing and gurgling
as sounds of contentment and joy.

· Baby will listen to voices when spoken to and respond accordingly.
With strangers she might cry or appear wary.
With Mom and Dad she will most likely smile or vocalize interest.

· The hearing abilities of a three-month-old are quite close to that of an adult.
Sound stimuli such as music, talking, television, and toys will attract their attention.

 Babies are not born to give love.
Babies are born to be loved.
Babies will learn to give love,
Only after being loved.

Thoughts on our baby at three months

_____

_____

_____

_____

_____

_____

_____

_____

_____

_____

_____

_____

_____

Photograph

Rock-A-Baby

Rock-a-Baby, Rock-a-Baby
Mama loves to rock her baby.
Baby's sleepy—Baby's tired
Close your eyes—I'll rock-a-baby.

Rock-a-Baby, Rock-a-Baby
Tiny sleeping little baby.
Mama loves you, Daddy loves,
Sleep in peace, I'll rock-a-baby.

My son, if your heart is wise,
then my heart will be glad;
my inmost being will rejoice
when your lips speak what is right.

Proverbs 23:15-16

Honor your father and your mother,
as the LORD your God has commanded you,
so that you may live long and that it may
go well with you in the land the LORD
your God is giving you.

Deuteronomy 5:16

A Temporary Caretaker

People often ask me what achievement I'm proudest of. I'd like to
answer that my children are my finest work, but of course, I know
they're not. God sent them to me, and I will be but their caretaker for a
little while. For all that is good and true in them, I must look to Him
with thanksgiving and wonder.

DING, DONG, BELL...

Come, my children, listen to me;
I will teach you the fear of the LORD.

Psalm 34:11

A Bear Named Kitty

(For Erik and Kitty—Love, Mama)

My name is Kitty, and I'm a bear!
A bear named Kitty? You say how rare.
The boy who owns me named me that, 'cause
my face is fluffy like a nice, fat cat.
The boy who loves me tells me too, and he
speaks in cat and says, "Mew-mew."
Sometimes the boy is sad and cries, and presses
his tears against my eyes.
But when he's happy we run and play, and sometimes we travel far away.
We climb up hills and ride in cars. We visit zoos and look at stars.
The boy who loves me takes me to bed, and when we sleep, we're head to head.
If he should have an awful dream and wake up with a cry or scream,
He holds me close like good friends do, and he calls "Mama," and I cry, "Mew."
Then Mama or Daddy come to see, and hold the little boy and me.
We snuggle down in arms that care, the little boy and his kitty-bear.
I shall always love my boy, and even though I'm just a toy,
I know he'll grow up, and more's the pity, then he won't need his bear named Kitty.
But while he's just a little boy, I know he's mine and oh, what joy!
My name is Kitty, and I'm just a bear, but I know love, and that's what's rare!

Babies at Four Months

· Babies at four months are a great deal of fun.
They are still not very active as far as getting around on their own;
however, they are quite interested in their environment.

· Four-month-olds are generally sleeping in a fairly well-established routine. Three to four daytime naps are pretty routine for baby at this age.

· Some doctors will introduce solids as early as four months,
suggesting you start with one item at a time and take it slow and easy.
Remember, there is no need to hurry solids, and most doctors will agree
that the older the baby is when he starts new foods, the less likely
he is to develop food allergies.

· Most babies at this stage will roll from stomach
to back and often from back to stomach.

Thoughts on our baby at four months

_____

_____

_____

_____

_____

_____

_____

_____

_____

_____

_____

_____

_____

_____

Photograph

A Daddy's Job

At the crib of his newborn daughter, a father once looked down in joy. He reached his hand out to feel the baby softness of her tiny face. He thought of all the days to come and, smiling tenderly, he said, " I am your Daddy. It is my job to walk ahead and let you know, the path to take, the way to go. I walk ahead to show you, too, that all is well and safe for you."

That tiny girl grew fast and strong. She learn to smile, to sit, to crawl. Her father watched her with "Daddy eyes," and when she began to walk, he calmly followed and sighed, "I am your Daddy. It is my job to walk behind in case you fall, to help you up whenever you call. I walk behind to show you, too, that some-one's always there for you."

It wasn't long before the father stood at his daughter's side. In radiant white, she clutched his arm, prepared to become a bride. He placed a kiss on his little girl's cheek, and with bittersweet joy he cried, "I am your Daddy. It is my job to walk beside, to hold your hand, to be supportive and understand. I walk beside to show you, too, that love will always bind me to you."

Years passed by, as years will do. In a quiet hospital room, the father lay dying, his daughter at his side. She kissed him gently and as her tears touched his weathered cheek, he smiled and said good-bye. "I am your Daddy. It is my job to walk ahead and let you know, the path to take, the way to go. I walk ahead to show you, too, that all is well and safe for you."

Your Daily Companion

The moment when I felt the most inadequate was when the nurse put my firstborn daughter Jennifer into my arms and sent me home to care for and nurture this tiny human being. Feelings of panic washed over me; shortcomings and misgivings that nine months of pregnancy had not been able to wipe out came rushing back to haunt me. What if I forget that I have her? What if I do something wrong? What if. . . ?

There is nothing quite so humbling as knowing that you are responsible for another life. But there is also nothing that fills your heart with more joy than to realize that out of your love for another, this perfect combination of man and woman has come to share your life. Fear is easily overcome by the realization that it serves no purpose but to destroy. Joy, on the other hand, is a strengthening agent, a powerful motivator, a hope for tomorrow. By pushing the fears aside and focusing on the love and joy, God is able to work miracles of contentment that might not otherwise have ever come. Life is too short to be consumed by fears—let joy, instead, be your daily companion.

The Best Celebration

*I*n our celebration of life, I will always remember my son's first Christmas and the teddy bear we gave him. Deciding to buy the fluffy gray bear as a last-minute gift, I didn't give the little furry fellow much thought. He was a teddy bear like any other, but something about him compelled me to take him home.

Little did I realize he would become my son's favorite toy and follow us through life in the years to come. Neither did I realize that this toy would be perceived not in the bear form intended by its maker, but rather as "Kitty," dubbed this by the boy who saw something else. Kitty has been an institution in our family for nearly as long as our son.

Kitty, who started out fluffy and fat, is now well-worn, sparsely covered, and after many surgical repairs, altered somewhat in appearance. But Kitty is loyal and true, and when others hurt my son, Kitty is faithful to bind his wounds.

Erik and Kitty remind me of the joy in simpler pleasures, of quiet moments with good friends and loving relationships where trust is the foundation. A celebration of life doesn't have to come with brass bands or expensive mementos; the best celebrations come in the form of a child's sweet smile, a mother's love, a father's guidance. And maybe even in the pudgy worn form of a stuffed bear named Kitty.

Time and Patience

An old Chinese proverb
reminds us that
"With time and patience,
the mulberry leaf becomes satin."
So, too, we should remember
that the infants in the cradles today,
will tomorrow be the leaders
and followers of our world.

Time will grow those children to adulthood,
but patience will be the foundation
on which we teach them the values
that will separate them
from the ordinary
into the truly fine.

Selfishness Is No Longer an Option

Selfishness and parenting do not mix. "Me first," will get you nowhere when dealing with infants. They do not understand the concept of self-gratification, self-indulgence, or self-introspection. Theories and philosophies are of very little concern compared to an empty stomach, a wet bottom, or teething gums. My mother always told me, "Don't even think of having children until you are ready to put them first." She also added, "After the baby arrives it's too late to decide that issue. Then it's no longer an option, but an absolute necessity."

A Precious Relationship

A mother knows her infant in a way that one else can know him. She hears the distress in his cries and knows the difference between a cry of irritation and boredom and a cry of pain or hunger. She reaches a point where no matter where she is, if she hears that cry from across the room, she will know and recognize immediately that the voice is that of her child calling out to her.

It is said that babies, too, come to recognize their mother's voices while even yet in the womb. A baby will listen when the mother speaks, and often the effect is calming, soothing, loving. A special bond is created between mother and baby even before that infant is received into the world, and from it comes a most precious relationship that no one else will ever share.

We, too, have a relationship like this with our loving Parent in heaven. He hears us whenever we call out to Him, and He understands exactly what we need. And as we spend more and more time with Him, we, too, will come to recognize His voice. A special bond will be created between us, the most precious relationship in the world.

. . .His sheep follow him because they know his voice. John 10:4

49

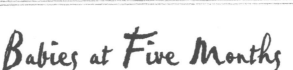

Babies at Five Months

· Five months is often the time when babies have a burst of growth and accomplishment. Feeding times become moments of entertainment and socializing. Baby will see this as one of the highlights of the day.

· Babies at this stage will often begin to form a specific manner of sleeping and no matter what position you put them in, they will adapt to what comforts them most.

· Babies will rock on their stomachs and maybe even draw their knees up as if to crawl. They will sit with support for as much as thirty minutes without overtiring and are capable of balancing their heads in a steady manner for continued periods of time.

· Often at this stage, babies will begin waking around 5 or 6 A.M., no matter what time they've been put to bed the night before. This is a normal stage and very little can be done to reset their inner clock.

Thoughts on our baby at five months

Photograph

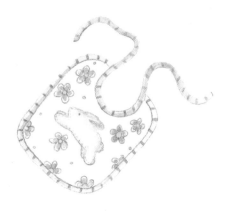

All Will Be Well

Holding a sleeping baby has to be one of life's better moments. To feel the steady, rhythmic breathing, to watch the pursed little lips quiver and move in sleepy sucking motions, shows me the overwhelming trust an infant places in her parents. Of course, she has no choice. She's too weak to fight. Too needy to refuse such care. She looks to us, as parents, for her all. Knowing that nothing can be done by herself to benefit her needs, she rests quietly in our arms.

That kind of trust reminds me of how it might be between God and His children. How we might rest in stillness, assured that our Father will oversee and meet our needs. That we can trust, aware of our weak inadequacies but confident that all will be well, that our Father is in charge and has already prepared for tomorrow.

A mother's love
endures
through all;
in good repute,
in bad repute.
In the face
of the world's
condemnation,
a mother
still loves on.
Washington Irving

And my God will meet all your needs according to his glorious riches in Christ Jesus.
Philippians 4:19

Fleeting Moments

First the touch,
    Then the smile,
Then my baby
    Is a little child.

Yesterday you wriggled,
    Today you walk,
Before I know it,
    My baby talks.

Growing moments,
    They come so fast,
How can I miss them,
    Let them slide past?

I'll be here, my little one,
    To carefully guide,
And each fleeting moment,
    I'll store lovingly inside.
        Carolyn R. Scheidies (© 1999)

Let's Be Honest

The sitcom ended with canned applause, and I crawled up from the couch, ready to do my usual garbage sweep through the living room as I headed toward the kitchen. Suddenly the television mother's image filled the screen—slender, designer-dressed, every hair in perfect place. I could almost smell her perfume.

"She's too classy to be real," I announced to no one in particular.

My husband lifted his brows.

"I mean, have you ever thought about it?" I continued. "There's not a real mother alive who is that classy."

I don't suppose we mothers can help it. Un-classiness is simply an occupational hazard.

· Classy women never show their toes in public.
Real mothers go barefoot as often as they can.

. . . .

· Classy women are always dressed up.
Real mothers don't comb their hair before lunch on Saturday and shed
their work clothes the moment they come through the door.

. . . .

· Classy women never yell.
Real mothers scream their heads off when their children are bleeding, playing
in a football game, or about to do something they aren't supposed to do.

· Classy women read newspapers and ten-pound tomes on
the *New York Times* best-seller list.
Real mothers read the comics first thing in the morning
and picture books at bedtime.
During lunch, mothers read dog-eared books about
how to discipline their children properly.

. . . .

· Classy women do not eat leftovers from their children's
plates or lick the spoon after mixing chocolate icing.
Real mothers do, and consequently gain two pounds
per child per year for the rest of their lives.

. . . .

· Classy women cook exotic entrees like lamb and goose.
Real mothers order truckloads of pizza and know that
thin hamburgers are better than thick ones.
In a pinch, though, they can whip up a bowl of spaghetti.

. . . .

· Classy women never lose their dignity.
Real mothers hang dignity in a closet and pull it out only
for family photos and parent-teacher conferences.

There was
never
a child
so lovely
but his
mother
was glad
to get him
to sleep.
Ralph Waldo
Emerson

· Classy women don't cry at the sight of baby pictures or
in hospital emergency rooms.
Real mothers do.

. . . .

· Classy women watch PBS specials on television while they sip tea.
Real mothers guard the television with a vigilant eye
and know which circuit breaker to flip if things ever get out of hand.

. . . .

· Classy women spend their evenings in quiet conversation with friends.
Real mothers spend their evenings with real fathers,
who know that nothing sends a child off to sleep faster
than the sound of parents laughing in the kitchen.

. . . .

· Classy women don't know how to change diapers,
make maps out of dryer lint,
or untangle a child's tongue from orthodontia.
Real mothers know everything.

I used to want to be a classy woman. I spent hours designing my hair, my wardrobe, my manners. I read all the books about dressing for success and speaking with confidence. I wanted to be a good representative of my Heavenly Father and King.

But then God sent two wonderful babies into my life and my priorities shifted.

It became more important to raise happy, healthy, respectful children who knew and loved the God who had brought them to me.

A few summers ago I served as a volunteer counselor at middle school camp. My daughter and I joined several other kids for a horseback trail ride. "What's the name of this horse?" I asked the guide as I swung into the saddle.

The trail guide grinned. "Classy."

What a horse. Surrounded by squealing kids, horseflies, and the thick stickiness of a Florida summer, she shifted under my weight and looked back at me with a calm, forgiving eye.

I leaned forward and patted her neck, then held my head high. I was as close to "Classy" as I ever wanted to be.

Angela Elwell Hunt (© 1999)

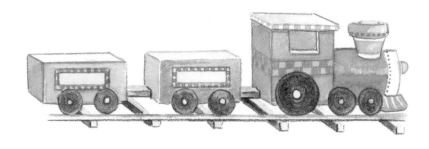

Blessed is the [mother] who makes the LORD [her] trust. . .
Psalm 40:4

Babies at Six Months

· Baby will usually cut her first teeth around this time.

· Sitting up becomes routine, and often pulling up to a standing position, especially in the crib, becomes a favorite form of entertainment.

· Babbling often takes the form of words, such as "Mama" and "Dada."

· Creeping, crawling, and other actions to move baby around the room are really starting to shape up by this age. Babies become much more active and mobile and, therefore, require closer observation.

Babies are proof of God's possibilities.
Where we see limitations and absolute impossibilities,
God sees potential and hope.
The Lord did for Sarah what He had promised.
He'll do the same for us.

Thoughts on our baby at six months

_____

_____

_____

_____

_____

_____

_____

_____

_____

_____

_____

_____

_____

Photograph

A Dear Teacher

Oftentimes in life, the most complicated things come with instruction manuals. Cars have them. VCRs have them. I even found instructions with my toaster. Babies, however, come without manuals or training courses. In the old days, long before television and educational videos, long before talk shows expounded on the latest "How to Be the Best Parent in the World" books, information and advice was handed down from mother to daughter and father to son.

Sometimes new parents shy away from asking old parents for advice. They feel proud or independent—and often they suffer miserably when help is just as close as the telephone. Even if a parent isn't around to seek advice from, there is always someone—a friend, a coworker, a brother or sister in the church. Don't let pride leave you in want. Experience is indeed a dear teacher.

Isaac prayed to the LORD on behalf of his wife, because she was barren. The LORD answered his prayer, and his wife Rebekah became pregnant.

Genesis 25:21

Photograph

Two Sides of the Same Coin

The babies jostled each other within her, and she said,
"Why is this happening to me?" So she went to inquire of the LORD.
The LORD said to her, "Two nations are in your womb,
and two peoples from within you will be separated;
one people will be stronger than the other,
and the older will serve the younger."
When the time came for her to give birth,
there were twin boys in her womb.
Genesis 25:22–24

Rebekah not only had her heart's deepest wish fulfilled in the birth of a child, but God gave out the abundance of His riches and blessed her with two babies. What wonder must have filled her when she realized that she was to become the mother of twins. Twin sons who would be both a joy and a heartache to her in the years to come.

That's the way motherhood is. Two sides of the same coin. Joy and sorrow. There will always be days when the heartaches come. Days when the messes seem too many to care for, when your child is sick and no one seems to know just what to do. But days of joy are just around the corner. Days of sweet delight with first steps and gazes of wonder. Times of happiness when your baby learns to talk and says, "I love you." Motherhood is full of these small moments of celebration.

Babies at Seven Months

· Baby's vision becomes more clear by this time.
She can generally see as well as older children.

· At seven months, a baby is able to hold toys or other objects in each
hand and will actively seek objects to play with.

· Babies at this age show true social interaction. They take on
a personality of their own, often showing themselves to be quite serious
and quiet, or humorous and silly. Interacting with parents and others
is vital to their well-being.

· A seven-month-old will generally try to feed herself with finger foods.
Sometimes this is a very messy battle, but it's important to her development
to allow some self-feeding.

· Crawling becomes more routine in some babies, while others may still be
wriggling or scooting across the floor to get where they want to go.

Thoughts on our baby at seven months

_____

_____

_____

_____

_____

_____

_____

_____

_____

_____

_____

_____

_____

Photograph

Impressions

These commandments that I give you today are to be upon your hearts. Impress them on your children. Talk about them when you sit at home and when you walk along the road, when you lie down and when you get up.

Deuteronomy 6:6–7

Impressions are made by taking a firm, fixed original and pressing it into soft, pliable material. As parents, we need to be that solid original. God's Word needs to be so accurately carved into our own hearts, that when we talk or walk or lie down or get up, we press His image into the hearts of our children. An impression can't be made if there is no original image in place.

Self-Doubts

Infancy is an awkward time of "firsts" in the life of a parent. You find yourself suddenly concerned with things that never even entered your mind before. "Am I doing this right?" "Will I know when something is wrong?" You find yourself constantly second-guessing situations without any real assurance that you're doing the job properly. Babies can't tell you where it hurts or what's troubling them, and every cry has the potential to become a personal assault on your self-confidence.

Don't allow it to defeat you. It's normal to feel overwhelmed and inadequate for the task. Rest assured that other parents have gotten up in the night to crying infants who seem to have no reasonable excuse for their howls of misery. Be attentive and minister to your baby's needs, but realize that there will be times when your baby can cry for no reason at all. Think of this old rhyme my grandmother's mother passed down: "Sometimes a baby cries for milk—sometimes for bottoms dry. Sometimes they cry because their sick—and sometimes they cry to cry."

And if you're ever feeling discouraged and overwhelmed, remember: You are not alone. God, our loving Parent, is with you, to help and guide. Ultimately, our children's well-being depends on Him, not us. Take time each day to rest yourself in Him. Celebrate His love for you.

1 Peter 5:7 Cast all your anxiety on him because he cares for you.

Mary's Song

My soul glorifies the Lord
and my spirit rejoices
in God my Savior,
for he has been mindful
of the humble state of his servant.
From now on
all generations will call me blessed,
for the Mighty One
has done great things for me—
holy is his name.
His mercy extends to those
who fear him,
from generation to generation.

Luke 1:46–50

I picture this lovely white room with baby cradles lined up one after another. Angels stand guard to their every need. These are the children who have been called apart—babies who before even being formed in the womb had caught the eye of God. As I look, I realize that each child ever made is here; they have all caught God's eye.

"These are extra special babies," I can almost hear God say. "They are each special to Me." No doubt they would need special earthly parents. Parents who would understand their particular uniqueness. Maybe this sandy-haired little girl would become a world-famous scientist. No doubt her withered arm would slow her down, but surely not by much. Or the dark-skinned boy in the corner—he's blind in sight, but one day he will lead thousands to the Lord through the rich fullness of his baritone voice. Or maybe just one single little girl. Perfect and healthy in every way, who will do nothing more than give her mother the will to continue living.

We are all set apart by God's hand for something very special. Have you found that reason for your life?

The word of the LORD came to me, saying, "Before I formed you in the womb I knew you, before you were born I set you apart."

Jeremiah 1:4-5

69

Loved within the Womb

For you have been my hope, O Sovereign LORD, my confidence since my youth.
From birth I have relied on you; you brought me forth from my mother's womb.
I will ever praise you.
Psalm 71:5–6

We can't remember the time in our mother's womb when God was our companion. But it must be so for the Psalms tell us that we relied upon Him from birth. I like to imagine angels whispering tender words to my unborn child. Perhaps that is why there were so many kicks and bumps. Perhaps they were all sharing a good story and laughing. Better still, perhaps they were given instructions—words of wisdom for the future.

A Husband's Prayers

How precious and sweet the prayers of a husband for his wife. Isaac must have known Rebekah's desire to bear a child. He surely heard her weeping, praying, pleading to God for a baby. Isaac took the matter to the one place where he knew he could get action. He took it to prayer. God saw Isaac's faith and love. Here was a man who wasn't afraid to get caught up in a "female problem." He loved his wife most dearly and took her heart's desire to his own heart—and to God.

Theodore Roosevelt once said,

"Into the woman's keeping
is committed the destiny
of the generations to come after us."

Mothers, never underestimate the power
you have in the task you perform.
Though it may seem less than
glamorous to spend your days cleaning messes
and wiping noses, the future generations
of our land are being molded by your instruction.

It's an awesome responsibility
and one which should never
be entered into lightly.

Babies at Eight Months

· At eight months almost everything goes into the mouth for a sample tasting. It's important, therefore, to keep tiny, harmful objects out of baby's reach and off the floor. An object doesn't need to be all that big at this age to induce choking.

· Crawling, pulling up, and even some walking can be the anticipated agenda for the eight-month-old. Mobility is the name of the game, and baby loves to be everywhere at once.

· Baby will begin to be afraid of strangers, and separation from loved ones will make him cry. Reassure him with extra love and affection.

Never scold a child for his fear.

· Babies at this age start to take real interest in toys and may play with an object for up to three or four minutes at a time.

Thoughts on our baby at eight months

Photograph

A Special
Birth Announcement

While they were there, the time came for the baby to be born,
and she gave birth to her firstborn, a son. She wrapped him in cloths
and placed him in a manger, because there was no room for them
in the inn. And there were shepherds living out in the fields nearby, keeping
watch over their flocks at night. An angel of the Lord appeared to them,
and the glory of the Lord shone around them, and they were terrified.
But the angel said to them, "Do not be afraid. I bring you good news of
great joy that will be for all the people. Today in the town of David a Savior
has been born to you; he is Christ the Lord. This will be a sign to you: You
will find a baby wrapped in cloths and lying in a manger." Suddenly a great
company of the heavenly host appeared with the angel, praising God
and saying, "Glory to God in the highest,
and on earth peace to men on whom his favor rests."
Luke 2:6–15

But Mary treasured up
all these things and pondered
them in her heart. Luke 2:19

Heart Treasures

As a new mother, many will be the times when you treasure up things in your heart. That first smile or laugh. The first time your baby sits up or crawls. Maybe it will come in the form of adoration offered by strangers or loved ones. "What a beautiful baby." "What a sweet-tempered child." Whatever constitutes "these things," like Mary, you will find them coming back to you as tender memories of your baby's life. They are treasures to be cherished.

A Father's Love

A father's role in the life of his infant is just as important as that of the mother. Fathers tend not to spend much time with babies, as they are often uncomfortable with these tiny bundles. They fear holding them too tightly or dropping them. Ultimately, familiarity will alleviate some of those fears. Fathers need to talk to their infants and show them tenderness and affection. They need to play with them, making faces, clapping baby's hands together, or using toys to hold their interest. A father's love is vital and should never be sacrificed because of time schedules or fears.

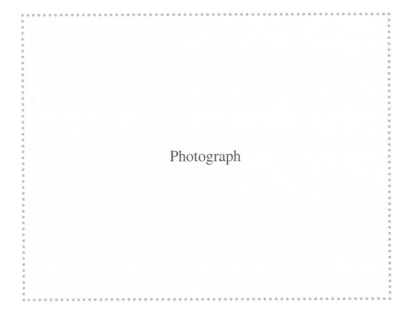

Photograph

Wisdom for the Asking

Directing the steps of a child is no easy task. It's not a job for the faint-hearted or easily wearied. Neither is it a task you can pick up one day and set down the next. It requires consistency, dedication, and love. In order for a child to pay attention to our wisdom, we must strive to be wise. God has promised to give wisdom to anyone who asks (James 1:5). As parents we need to seek this wisdom with our whole hearts. Our job is one of tremendous responsibility and our childrens' well-being is in the balance.

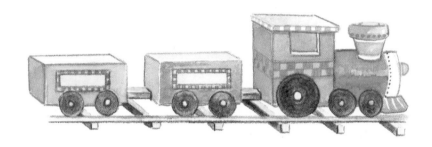

My son, pay attention to my wisdom,
listen well to my words of insight,
that you may maintain discretion
and your lips may preserve knowledge.

Proverbs 5:1-2

Photograph

There is only
one pretty child
in the world,
and every mother
has it.
Old English proverb

Men want to improve
only the world;
but mothers want
to improve their
whole family. That is
a much harder task.
Anonymous

Photograph

Listen, my son, accept what I say,
and the years of your life will be many.
I guide you in the way of wisdom
and lead you along straight paths.
When you walk, your steps will not be hampered;
when you run, you will not stumble.

Proverbs 4:10-12

A Journey of Love

My heart will ever be a road map of my mother-hood. Here is the place where my journey began—my baby's first cry of life. Here is the place where we stopped for repairs—my baby's first scraped knee when learning to walk. Here is the place where we took our rest—a quiet moment of evening prayers when my toddler thanked God for cookies. There are bumpy roads and smooth, quiet respites and busy freeways, but always it is a journey that I set myself upon because of one thing—a deep abiding love for my children. And that alone, makes the journey full of joy.

Babies at Nine Months

· Babies at nine months show real interest in conversations. Sometimes they will try to communicate with one or two words as language improves.

· Babies at this age are generally able to sit without any assistance and may have begun to point at objects with their index finger.

· Nine months often is the time when babies begin to perform for parents or others. They will watch for approval, and if they sense amusement or encouragement, will often repeat an action several times for the benefit of the laughter or applause.

· Fears are heightened at this age as the baby begins to gain a sense of vertical space.

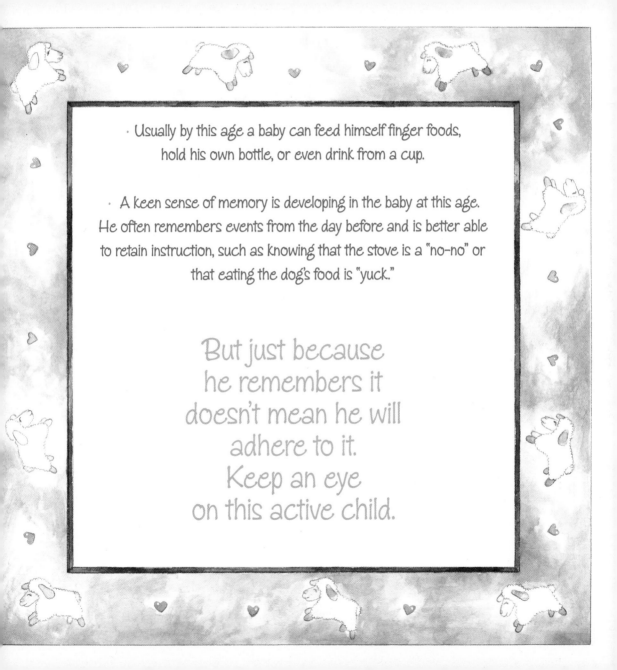

· Usually by this age a baby can feed himself finger foods, hold his own bottle, or even drink from a cup.

· A keen sense of memory is developing in the baby at this age. He often remembers events from the day before and is better able to retain instruction, such as knowing that the stove is a "no-no" or that eating the dog's food is "yuck."

But just because
he remembers it
doesn't mean he will
adhere to it.
Keep an eye
on this active child.

Thoughts on
our baby at
nine months

_____

_____

_____

_____

_____

_____

_____

_____

_____

_____

_____

_____

Photograph

Photograph

My [child], keep your
father's commands
and do not forsake
your mother's teaching.
Bind them upon your heart
forever; fasten them
around your neck.
When you walk,
they will guide you;
when you sleep,
they will watch over you;
when you awake, they will
speak to you.
Proverbs 6:20–22

A Miracle

A miracle takes place in our lives when a child is born. A new life comes forth from the old, but not only this, the anguish of intense pain is laid aside at the sight of our baby. God created us in a unique and marvelous way. He balanced the pain of childbirth with the wonder of new life and love and a hope so eternal that even hours of labor suddenly seem unimportant in the light of what He has done.

Few people think that the management
of very young babes has anything to do
with their future dispositions and characters;
yet I believe it has more influence
than can easily be calculated.
Lydia Maria Child

Proverbs
23:22

Listen
to your father,
who gave you
life, and do not
despise your
mother
when she is old.

Teaching Peace and Joy

Children often take their cues from adults. Watch a baby learning to walk and then watch the expression on the face of the parents. If the parent looks sad or upset when the baby falls, the child will often pout or cry. If the parent claps and encourages baby to try again, often the baby will laugh and spring back up with great enthusiasm.

Even so, young children will imitate other things they see in us as well. If we are angry when dealing with material objects or other people, children will often mimic that same attitude in play.

It's important to let your children see the positive. When things go wrong, they will watch to see how you respond. If something frightening happens, they often don't realize there is any problem at all until they see your face or hear the fear in your voice.

Teaching children to walk and talk is vital to their development, but teaching them to handle the little interruptions or excitements of life is just as important. Remember, their eyes are always watching, and even at very young ages, they are taking mental notes on how to deal with life.

Why not teach them to celebrate God's goodness, right from the beginning?

Babies at Ten Months

· By now, many ten-month-olds are walking on their own. Some hold on to things for extra support, while others toddle off across the room. There is no reason to rush a child who is still in the crawling stage, however. Babies will develop in their own time and way. One may walk at nine months and another at fifteen months. It's all a matter of their personal development, and they shouldn't be hurried.

· Babies at ten months can usually climb up and down from chairs or stairs.

· Vocabulary and actions are ever increasing. Babies will often say "no" and "bye-bye" at ten months, and will often wave, give kisses and hugs, and shake their heads "no."

· The ten-month-old is moving ever more rapidly toward independence and may even try to help her parents when they are dressing or undressing her.

· Often during this period of life a baby will form a special bond or attachment to a favorite toy or blanket.

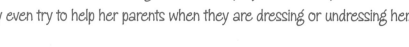
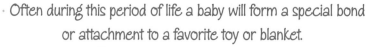

Thoughts on our baby at ten months

_____

_____

_____

_____

_____

_____

_____

_____

_____

_____

_____

_____

_____

_____

Photograph

An Inheritance from the Lord

Joy!—overshadowed with a nagging feeling that in spite of our daughter having just been born, God wanted us to have yet another, another son. Being practical—that was out of the question. We had one son and one daughter, our family was complete. Fifteen months later I'm in the same delivery room, giving birth to the son God said we would have.

Children are a blessing and an inheritance from the Lord. I've thought back often to my arrogant days of thinking we were to have only two children. But God wanted more. Why? Because of the inheritance—the blessing, the joy, the pain, the patience, the learning that only that third child would bring into our lives.

He is fully grown now, a man, married and one day to be a father himself. Babies are the adventure of a lifetime, an inheritance from the Lord.

Lynn A. Coleman

What Will You Be?

When you grow up what will you be?
Will you be tall like Dad or short like me?
Will your hair be dark like it is right now?
Or will it turn amber, or auburn, or brown?

Will you run fast with agility and grace?
Or fall behind in a slower pace?
Will words come quickly to your mouth and hand?
Or will mathematics and numbers be your plan?

Whatever you choose and wherever you go,
May you always understand and know,
That you are loved, not for what you do,
But because you're special—because you're you.

Mothers and Babies

For nine months I waited, I watched and I planned,
Always wondering how it would be,
That you would arrive, a new life all alone,
So helpless—dependent on me.

And now you are here, and I see for myself,
That a new slate of questions have come,
Will I do the right thing? Will I know what you need?
Will I know when a thing is undone?

You open your eyes and look into mine,
And a great world of trust is reflected,
But I know nothing of being a mother to you,
There's so much that should be perfected.

Then you smile at me and the fears seem to fade,
And I wonder just what you might say.
If you knew all my worries, concerns, and desires—
The hours I've knelt down to pray.

I reach for your hand, so tiny and soft,
And I see that we're in the same place.
You look up to me for your comfort and help.
I look up to God for His grace.

Mothers and babies are not quite so different.
The lesson I've learned is quite clear.
Both seek to find comfort, assurance, and love,
And to know their Protector is near.
Anonymous

Babies at Eleven Months

· Babies at this age are generally up and running in a very mobile fashion. They explore everything and often have little fear of what they are doing.

· Eleven-month-old toddlers are usually very aware of their surroundings. They know their place in the family and have a good working knowledge of everyone else's position as well. Their relationships are developing into strong, meaningful encounters, and often they will seek approval.

· Babies at eleven months will often imitate sounds. They might meow for the cat or bark for the dog. They might make silly sounds or imitate things they see on television. Often an eleven-month-old will put more than one word together to make her first sentences: "Mama go." "Me, too." "Go bye-bye."

*Thoughts on
our baby at
eleven months*

Photograph

Teach [God's laws] to your children and to their children after them.

Deuteronomy 4:9

Cherish the Years

The best advice I can offer to new parents and old is to cherish your children. Look to each day as a new adventure in a very long journey. Think of their needs, consider their desires, make choices based on sound judgments rather than on what is easy and quick. The babies you hold today will be toddlers at full run tomorrow and teenagers with dreams and goals of their own in a shorter time than you can imagine. Hold them. . .teach them. . .guide them. . .but above all, love them. Don't let the years slip by so that you must reflect back on what might have been. Instead, live so that you can always delight in what has come to be.

Photograph

Baby's Handprints

A baby is an artistic extension
of a masterpiece in progress.

Tiny baby
sleeping there
In mother's arms,
without a care,
May you know
that you are loved,
By Mom and Dad
and God above.

Babies at Twelve Months

· Babies at twelve months are generally perceived as toddlers.
They are very mobile and often quite daring. They attempt running,
although they are not always very good at it. They climb and jump
and often appear to be everywhere at once.

· By twelve months, with repeated practice, a baby can use a cup and
often a spoon. Self-feeding, although messy, is to be encouraged.
However, this is also the time when some babies begin to refuse
certain foods and schedules for meals.

· Memory is greatly improved. Babies at this age will often remember
the routine from the day before.

· Twelve months is the start of a whole new world for your child.
She is rapidly passing from infancy into becoming a child of capability
and varied interests. Her personality is well-shaped and
she is uniquely herself.

Thoughts on our baby at twelve months

Photograph

Children are natural mimics
who act like their parents
in spite of every attempt
to teach them good manners.
Anonymous

A silent influence,
which they do not perceive,
is better for young children
than direct rules and prohibitions.
Lydia Maria Child,
The Mother's Book

Reflections of a Father's Heart

Date: _____

Things I want you to know about me:

_____

_____

_____

Things I want to say about you:

_____

_____

_____

Things I hope for your future:

_____

_____

_____

My prayer for you:

_____

_____

_____

Ten Things to Never Do with a Toddler

1. Never leave toddlers unsupervised. Children are designed with a curiosity that outweighs their ability to reason. If you think they might get into something, chances are they will.

2. Never communicate by yelling and screaming. The day may come when a warning in a raised voice is necessary to save their lives, but if screaming and yelling is the normal mode of communication, a child will ignore the urgency and treat the situation as status quo.

3. Never assume your toddler will behave in a routine/normal/textbook manner. Just the minute you think you can count on them to behave a certain way, they will do exactly the opposite.

4. Never use food as a punishment or reward. This puts undue importance on food and may well develop eating disorders in the years to come.

5. Never fail to be consistent. Children learn by actions and repetition. If you tell them the hot stove is "no" then tell them the cold stove is "no" as well. This way consistency teaches them that the stove is off-limits under any circumstance.

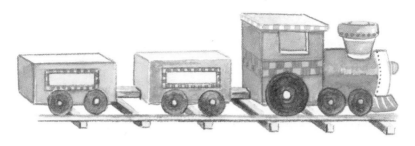

6. Never allow toddlers to play with objects intended for older children or adults. Glass and ceramics are easily broken and generally are easily replaced, but a wounded child is harder to deal with.

7. Never forget to praise your toddler. Reinforce good behavior with approval.

8. Never put your toddler in danger. A lot of parents might scoff at this, believing themselves incapable of doing such a thing, but this includes leaving a child unattended in a grocery cart, leaving a child in the car while you run in the store to get "one" thing, allowing an inappropriate person (such as another child) to watch over your toddler while you do something else, and not properly securing your toddler for car travel.

9. Never punish in anger. Toddlers can't understand the reasons behind your demands, and they are just as unable to understand the reason behind your anger. Keep your temper and remember just who's the grown-up and who's the child.

10. Never forget to love them. Tell them you love them with words. Show them you love them with actions. You can never give too much love.

Treasure Each Moment

When my daughter Julie was born, the doctors found a mysterious infection in her body that they seemed unable to defeat. She was put on medications, poked with needles to draw blood samples, and isolated away from me and her father. It was the hardest thing in the world to leave the hospital without her. My arms were empty, my heart ached in a way that nothing, not even my oldest daughter Jennifer, could fill.

I wandered around in a daze. Would my baby live or die? Would she come home to me soon, or would the medicine fail to heal? I longed for answers that no one could give me, and in my despair I turned to God. He was the only one who could help me. I prayed for one more day. One more day to know Julie better. One more day to perfect our love. And when that day passed and the dawn of a new day arrived, I prayed that same prayer over again. "One more day, Lord. Just give us one more day." I came to realize how precious time could be. That I needed to focus on the moment, and not on the questionable tomorrows.

Our daughter healed and came home, and I rejoiced in answered prayer. But I also came to realize that all we ever truly have is the present. Celebrate the joy you have been given right now. Cherish each moment.

> I love these little people; and it is not a slight thing,
> when they, who are so fresh from God, love us.
> Charles Dickens

See that
you do not look
down on one
of these
little ones.
For I tell you
that their angels
in heaven
always see
the face of
my Father
in heaven.
Matthew 18:10

It is important
that children,
even when babes,
should never be
spectators of anger,
or any evil passion.
They come to us from heaven,
with their little souls
full of innocence
and peace;
and, as far as possible,
a mother's influence
should not interfere
with the influence
of angels.
Lydia Maria Child

Lock of Hair

Date _____

Now the LORD was gracious to Sarah as he had said, and the LORD did for Sarah what he had promised. Sarah became pregnant and bore a son to Abraham in his old age, at the very time God had promised him.

Genesis 21:1–2

All that I am or hope to be, I owe to my mother.

Abraham Lincoln

In those moments when I cannot be with my babies, I have often turned to God in prayer. "I might not know where they are at just this moment, but You do. Guard them, keep them safe, watch over them in Your loving kindness." Such comfort has come to me just in knowing that God can see them, even when I cannot, and that He can care for them when it is beyond my ability to reach them.

God Is Always There

Fathers and mothers play very distinct roles in the lives of their babies. That's why it is the best of all possible arrangements to have both parents active in the life of their child. Often, this isn't the case. People die. People leave. And because of this, both sides struggle. But God has promised to be a father to the fatherless and to comfort His people as a mother comforts her child.

In those times of trying to raise a child without a partner, God will very neatly fill the void—if we will but allow Him that position. He may come in the form of comfort, internal peace, or joy that allows you to see beyond the circumstances of your life. He may come in the form of other people—human helpers who have been inspired by God to offer assistance in various ways. But whichever way God chooses to come to you—rest assured He is there for you. We are not asked to bear anything alone.

I will not leave you as orphans: I will come to you.

John 14:18

Celebrate Your Family

I hope your celebration of life is as happy as the one I've shared with my three children. Jennifer, my firstborn, was the beginning of a wondrous adventure. She taught me many things about life—lessons that often came in the form of trial and error as I raced through the new territory of motherhood. Julie, my second born, continued the journey and showed me paths that moved at a slower pace, as I learned to see life through different eyes. Erik, my third child and only son, sent me even farther down the road. He gave me a knowledge of the differences in boys and girls and produced enough energy to run a major metropolitan city.

The journey isn't over, however. Every day is something new. Sometimes we rejoice and sometimes we cry. We share our goals and dreams, and we bear one another's burdens and miseries. We are family—just as you and your children are.

So let's celebrate!

Father, bless my children, I pray. Watch over them and guard them,
keep them in Your care. Help them to be all that You have planned for them to be.
Give them sight to see the bad and good, and wisdom to make sound choices
between the two. Help them to know that even when bad times come,
You can see beyond the darkness and You will deliver them.
Wash them with love to help them realize that they are never alone.
Help them to always find reason to celebrate life's joy. Amen

About the Author

TRACIE PETERSON is author of over thirty inspirational fiction titles. As a Christian, wife, mother, and writer (in that order), Tracie finds her slate quite full. Tracie resides in Topeka, Kansas with her family. First published as a columnist for the *Kansas Christian Newspaper,* Tracie resigned that position to turn her attention to writing novels. Besides several inspirational romances with Heartsong Presents and Barbour Publishing, she has titles co-written with author Judith Pella as well as single titles published by Bethany House Publishers. Tracie also teaches workshops at a variety of conferences, giving talks on inspirational romance, historical research, and other areas of interest that offer assistance to fellow writers.